CONGRATULATIONS

You've Just
Passed
Grade *1*

PHONE

When The Saints Go Marching In

Traditional

Jeepers Creepers

Words by Johnny Mercer
Music by Harry Warren

I'm Looking Over A Four Leaf Clover

Words by Mort Dixon
Music by Harry Woods

Bye Bye Blackbird

Words by Mort Dixon
Music by Ray Henderson

4

My Heart Will Go On
(Love Theme from 'Titanic')

Words by Will Jennings
Music by James Horner

Pennsylvania 6-5000

Words and Music by Carl Sigman and Jerry Gray

Rudolph The Red-Nosed Reindeer

Words and Music by Johnny Marks

Blue Moon

Words by Lorenz Hart
Music by Richard Rodgers

I'm Forever Blowing Bubbles

Words and Music by Jaan Kenbrovin and John William Kellette

Scarborough Fair

Traditional

8

(Meet) The Flintstones

Words and Music by William Hanna, Joseph Barbera and Hoyt Curtin

On The Street Where You Live

Words and Music by Alan Jay Lerner
Music by Frederick Loewe

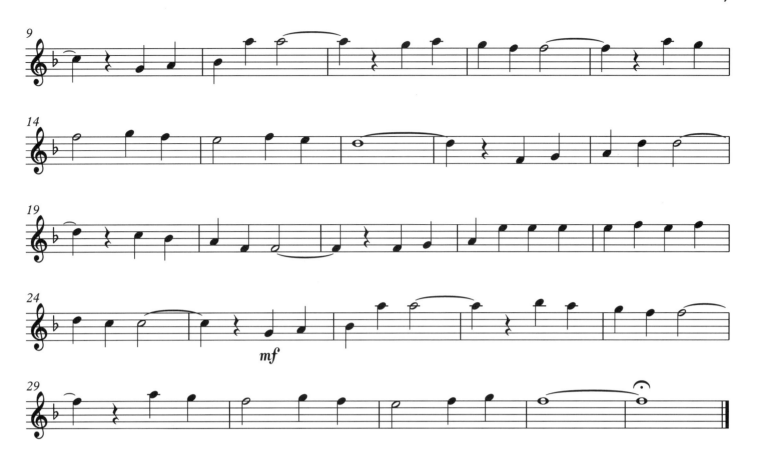

Basin Street Blues

Words and Music by Spencer Williams

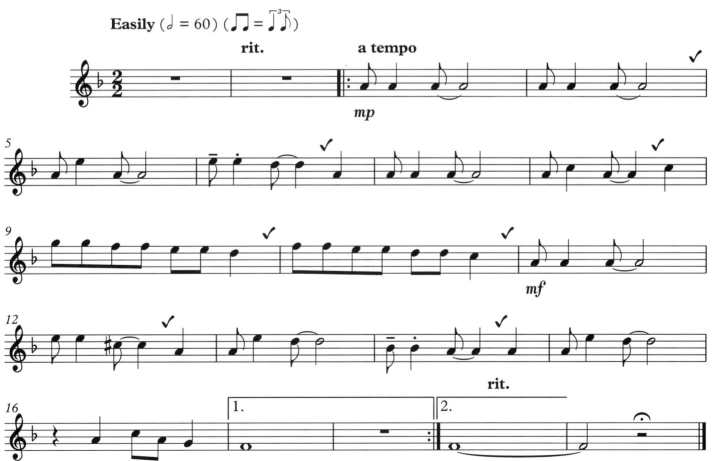

Angels

Words and Music by Robbie Williams and Guy Chambers

I Don't Want To Miss A Thing

Words and Music by Diane Warren

© 1998 & 1999 Realsongs, USA
EMI Music Publishing Ltd, London WC2H 0EA

How Do I Live

Words and Music by Diane Warren

Printed by
Halstan & Co. Ltd., Amersham, Bucks., England

7·50

CONGRATULATIONS!
You've Just Passed Grade 1

ALTO SAXOPHONE

	PIANO PART	ALTO SAXOPHONE PART
ANGELS	26	10
BASIN STREET BLUES	24	9
BLUE MOON	14	6
BYE BYE BLACKBIRD	6	3
(MEET) THE FLINTSTONES	20	8
HOW DO I LIVE	30	12
I DON'T WANT TO MISS A THING	28	11
I'M FOREVER BLOWING BUBBLES	16	6
I'M LOOKING OVER A FOUR LEAF CLOVER	4	2
JEEPERS CREEPERS	3	2
MY HEART WILL GO ON (LOVE THEME FROM 'TITANIC')	8	4
ON THE STREET WHERE YOU LIVE	22	8
PENNSYLVANIA 6-5000	10	4
RUDOLPH THE RED-NOSED REINDEER	12	5
SCARBOROUGH FAIR	18	7
WHEN THE SAINTS GO MARCHING IN	2	1

Exclusive distributors:

International Music Publications Germany: Marstallstrasse 8, D-80539 München, Germany
Danmusik: Vognmagergade 7, DK-1120 Cioenhage K, Denmark
Nuova Carisch Srl.: Via Campania, 12, San Giuliano Milanese, Milano, Italy
Carisch France, SARL: 20, rue de la Ville-l'Eveque, 75008 Paris, France
Nueva Carisch Espana S.L.: Via Magallenes 25, 28015 Madrid, Spain

Production: Sadie Cook and Miranda Steel

Music arranged and processed by Barnes Music Engraving Ltd
East Sussex TN22 4HA, England

Cover design by xheight design limited

Published 1999

International
MUSIC
Publications

International Music Publications Limited
Griffin House 161 Hammersmith Road London W6 8BS England

When The Saints Go Marching In

Traditional

Jeepers Creepers

Words by Johnny Mercer
Music by Harry Warren

I'm Looking Over A Four Leaf Clover

Words by Mort Dixon
Music by Harry Woods

Bye Bye Blackbird

Words by Mort Dixon
Music by Ray Henderson

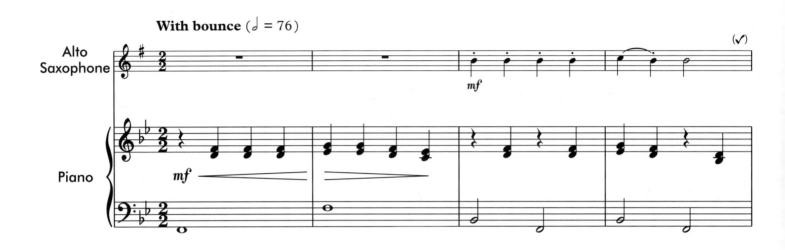

My Heart Will Go On
(Love Theme from 'Titanic')

Words by Will Jennings
Music by James Horner

Pennsylvania 6-5000

Words and Music by Carl Sigman and Jerry Gray

Rudolph The Red-Nosed Reindeer

Words and Music by Johnny Marks

Blue Moon

Words by Lorenz Hart
Music by Richard Rodgers

I'm Forever Blowing Bubbles

Words and Music by Jaan Kenbrovin and John William Kellette

Moderate waltz ($\quarternote$ = 132)

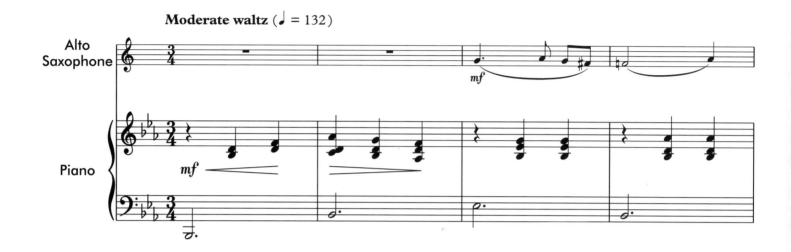

Scarborough Fair

Traditional

(Meet) The Flintstones

Words and Music by William Hanna, Joseph Barbera and Hoyt Curtin

On The Street Where You Live

Words and Music by Alan Jay Lerner
Music by Frederick Loewe

Basin Street Blues

Words and Music by Spencer Williams

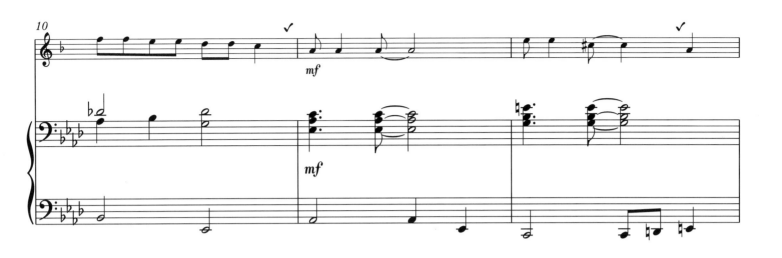

Angels

Words and Music by Robbie Williams and Guy Chambers

I Don't Want To Miss A Thing

Words and Music by Diane Warren

How Do I Live

Words and Music by Diane Warren

Printed by
Halstan & Co. Ltd., Amersham, Bucks., England